Notes from

Dr. Lucifer's Lectures

The Art of Leadership and Control 101

The Rev. James F. Graner

Note for Librarians: a cataloguing record for this book that includes Dewey
Decimal Classification and US Library of Congress numbers is available from the
Library and Archives of Canada. The complete cataloguing record can be obtained
from their online database at:
www.collectionscanada.ca/amicus/index-e.html
ISBN 1-4120-4716-1
Printed in Victoria, BC, Canada

TRAFFORD

Offices in Canada, USA, Ireland, UK and Spain
This book was published *on-demand* in cooperation with Trafford Publishing.
On-demand publishing is a unique process and service of making a book available
for retail sale to the public taking advantage of on-demand manufacturing and
Internet marketing. On-demand publishing includes promotions, retail sales,
manufacturing, order fulfilment, accounting and collecting royalties on behalf of the
author.
Book sales for North America and international:
Trafford Publishing, 6E–2333 Government St.,
Victoria, BC v8t 4p4 CANADA
phone 250 383 6864 (toll-free 1 888 232 4444)
fax 250 383 6804; email to orders@trafford.com
Book sales in Europe:
Trafford Publishing (uk) Ltd., Enterprise House, Wistaston Road Business Centre,
Wistaston Road, Crewe, Cheshire cw2 7rp UNITED KINGDOM
phone 01270 251 396 (local rate 0845 230 9601)
facsimile 01270 254 983; orders.uk@trafford.com
Order online at:
www.trafford.com/robots/04-2524.html

10 9 8 7 6 5 4 3 2

Preface

This little book is set with ample margins for your personal notes which we hope you will feel necessary to make as you read along and find things to remember or check out. It is designed to be read in little segments or all at once. We hope it will challenge you to see your own temptations and recognize the efforts of others to exert leadership and control over you. Being knowledgeable about techniques is your best defense against being duped so we went to the master himself to discover how it is done.

Foreword
The Art of Leadership and Control 101
(a.k.a. Lucifer's Lectures)

The Very Reverend Forrest Burgett
Rector of Trinity Anglican Church
Prairie Village, Kansas

Our world is a confusing place to the Traditional Christian mind set. Our Forefathers wisely established a concept entitled "Freedom of Religion" to insure that all religious practice had equal access to our government. Today, we are experiencing "Freedom from Religion" and, practicing the concepts described in this little book; those in control call it "Separation of Church and State". In literally every major expression of the Christian Faith, standards are being questioned.

Biblical prohibitions that were once universally accepted, are not only violated; they are promoted and glorified as a new standard of human achievement. Those attempting to maintain traditional, biblical views are depicted as mean-spirited and elitist.

How did we reach this state of development when worldwide communications can be handled in microseconds? As one might imagine, it is of human origin and not technological at all. Fr. Graner uses imaginary lectures from Lucifer to teach the concept. He describes the human frailties and desires that make the process possible. With tongue firmly in cheek, he points out the pertinent factors that must be balanced and adjusted to achieve the necessary dependencies. He illustrates the necessity of changing focus and definitions to maintain the illusion of benefit to those being led. He shows the need for economic controls to cement religious affiliation and discourage defections. These lectures will remain a "Do-It-Yourself" guide to Leadership and Control as long as people are willing to surrender their doctrine of moral conduct for the right to belong.

These lectures of Lucifer are truly imaginary. Otherwise, this would be a security leak of monumental proportions. This delightful book is enlightening as a comment on the human condition. However, it is best

when read repeatedly   until the
nuances and subtleties described
within are readily recognized in the
world around us.

Fr. Forrest Burgett
SS Simon and Jude, 2004

Table of Contents
A Satire - Dr. Lucifer's Lectures

(I'm no C. S. Lewis ...
he did an excellent Satire...
Here's my attempt.)

Notes From Dr. Lucifer's Lectures
The Art of Leadership and Control
101
Collected and retold

INTRODUCTION

As we consider this material we are about to cover, the first thing we must ALWAYS remember is that this is all about <u>Man</u>, in the generic sense, about how he sees himself and the world about him. Man consists of creatures of limited capacity for understanding and it is the charitable and urgent duty of the gifted few of this world (of which YOU may be a primary example) to organize, instruct, direct, and control the less fortunate people of the world. You will thank me for this later because

I was instrumental in introducing this element into Man's make-up. Man is self-aware (more on this later) and responds immediately to personal physical needs and discomforts, usually without consideration for abstract concepts of corporate needs or benefits unless well-trained to value these above self. This element is known as greed. Your job will be to provide a mix of values that brings this element under your direction and leadership. To organize, instruct, and direct, one must establish control.

Practical Considerations

To control, you must understand the nature of the being you intend to organize, instruct, and direct. You must take in consideration some factors that, while disturbing to the process we pursue, are necessary ground rules, which are fundamental realities that cannot be avoided.

The adversary to our pursuit of absolute control is God. His advantage stems from the fact that He created Man and consequently built in some qualities that we cannot change although we can use many to our advantage if managed properly. The major aid to avoiding this adversarial influence is sin, which has, by my brilliant effort, already been effectively introduced into the equation. Sin is the unqualified determination to be entirely self-determining, self-sufficient and physically comfortable, or as nearly so as possible. In other words, it is Man's unwillingness for God to be in control even though it is inevitable.

This introduces another essential point: Man is a created being, which means he is less than self-sufficient and responds readily to opportunities to realize benefits he cannot create for himself. In brief, he is greedy. This he sees as self-determination even though it is actually a surrender of some degree of self-control, which, of course, you will gladly accept in exchange for the benefits you can bestow.

4

Fortunately, in the immediacy of life, the desire for physical comforts (sufficient food, shelter, and freedom of movement and self-expression) is a strong short-term motivator for Man and these are weapons you can readily use in your pursuit of control. So strong is Man's desire for these benefits, he will readily surrender some elements of self-sufficiency for even a promise of benefits he holds more valued than that which he surrenders. Some training in benefit values can readily be employed to your advantage.

The downside of this is that when people become physically comfortable, that is, when the burdens become tolerable in relation to their benefits, they begin to look for abstract and promised benefits and comforts, something religion alone seems able to promise over a long-term period without a need for an immediate evidence of fulfillment. This is called hope, a built-in to Man that is one of God's strongest weapons against our establishing total control when introduced in the realm of ideals and enhanced corporate values. At this point, economic welfare and physical comforts often become a secondary consideration in the process of control.

Enter the need for religion.

The most effective element in the controlling process is to establish a religious basis for commitment. To do this we must establish a concept of an extra, or super-natural being outside the perceived world order whose realm is the consummate place of all that is perfect, meaningful, ideal, peaceful, non-threatening, enjoyable, healthy, and honorable, the realization of all that is hoped for, and then claim to be a primary or exclusive channel for revelation of that entity's will for achieving the benefits that being can conceptually bestow. This is a very strong control factor and is called religion. It is even more powerful than the economic motivator insofar as the economic benefits are more readily gauged and discounted by comparative evidence of material factors.

Generally speaking this can be established by assigning the mystical qualities of any misunderstood or un-explainable events in the perceived order to an entity (generally labeled to be a god) for which you claim to be the oracle. Observing patterns in phenomena such as wind, rain, moon, sun, animal behavior, and other such, permits you to predict or "speak for" these unknown and apparently mystical or spiritual entities to the more simple-minded masses of people, thus exerting a degree of control. These areas of control can be compounded and expanded rather easily once the pattern of control is established.

Besides the observations of the natural order and the opportunities for control they present, a more sophisticated and powerful tool is found in the area of abstracts. Things perceived to be happy or sad, beneficial or destructive, can be converted into spiritual concepts and entities of good and evil, which can then be channeled into very powerful religious factors for directing and controlling behavior of the followers you acquire. It also has an obtuse, or diffused base, which can be manipulated with relative ease by redirecting the perception of the object of the beneficial or distressful action in question. For example, demonstrating that an individual may find a given precept burdensome, the benefit normally derived for the society as a whole can be dismissed as a motivating factor for the good when the people are led to think of the individual as the central unit for which the religion exists. While this action permits temporary gains, it is intrinsically self-destructive because the process of satisfying the desires of each individual of necessity impinges the benefits to other individuals and/or the group as a whole and the inherent conflict of interests will cause a breakdown of the controllable religious groups. The infusion of such concepts as the undesirability of schism may for a while deter the breakdown but the burden of self-destructive behavior imposed by the requirement to permit individual expression of patterns destructive to the group welfare will in the end bring a breakdown of the religious unit.

On the other hand, individuals who find the precepts of the religion burdensome to their personal preferences and lifestyles will either avoid the control group or eventually leave it if they are not shown and taught benefits of greater value to them than suffering the real or imagined burden of any discomforts associated with the teachings. Many a leader because of his incompetence has sacrificed a viable religious establishment by attempting to cater to individual discomforts at the expense of the group welfare rather than take the time and effort to teach and re-enforce essential benefits of greater value than the precepts causing the individuals distress.

The above does not discount the fact that when establishing religious precepts that have to do with personal conduct, such as the 10 Commandments, for example, even though these religious precepts become widely accepted and codified into secular law, there are still options available to you.

Codes of conduct always present codes of punishment for disobedience and religions always provide a means of escaping the punishment, usually in the form of opportunities for forgiveness. As spokesperson for the religious entity you represent, relaxing or changing the criteria by which the rule is understood or enforced, you can gradually reverse the rule, or at least, render it impotent to those offended or burdened by it. This technique is simply the process of changing the priority system of the group. For example, the interpretation of adultery amongst Christians for many centuries was that divorced persons could not remarry in the church because it constituted adultery. This ruling has been eroded by abuse propagated by their religious leaders in recent years so that even those in office as high as bishop find remarriage after divorce an acceptable norm. Homosexuality, once denounced in many Christian bodies based upon Biblical evidence, has in some places acquired not only acceptance, but the practice also receives assistance in trying to adjust secular law to support the practice.

In more sophisticated societies, there may be accommodations necessary for other groups of similar structure to co-exist within a common economic framework. At this point, it is necessary to acquire the stronger economic position of ownership or control so that those who are using religion for control will need your favor to continue their portion of control. This allows you to maintain a central control over a multiplicity of religious factions. You should attempt to make the dominant group your "official and centrally supported" religion to assure its leadership is more securely dependent upon you. This is called government and can be of any form such as monarchy, dictatorship, democracy, shamanism, or tribal chief.

In some cases, when the governing entity can assume an identity as the protector and enforcer or in some cases as the prophet or oracle of the religious revealed revelation or law within the society, it is possible to eliminate all religious units that profess any differing source of revelation. This permits a dictatorial control that is both religious and economic and approximates the desirable end of absolute control. Unfortunately, this event almost always involves the use of fear and military oversight with considerable oppression and brutality. This imposes an unbearable burden, which eventually results in a war like rebellion and all is lost.

Choosing your style

When establishing an economically dependent religion, it is necessary to maintain some degree of control over the revelation process to assure that your position is necessary in the process of obtaining the promises of the established religious commitment. This can be done in several ways: sanctifying parcels of land mass as "holy ground" for a particular people, establishing ethnic continuity by racial identity, establishing fidelity to a heroic figure from the past (real or devised for convenience), or securing fidelity to a present heroic personage although this latter option has a transitory quality that is difficult to maintain for more than a single generation.

The more diverse the society and variety of religious communities becomes, the more diffused becomes the leadership capabilities. Two basic styles of leadership emerge readily from this diversity and you must make a decision as to which best suits your personal ability. One style is essentially congregational and contemporary in that each community elects its own leader and the revelation it is most comfortable with. The other style is corporate and historical which is passed from generation to generation with an essential credo and identifiable historical body of revelation. Between these two poles lies an infinite range of degrees of combined qualities.

In the corporate style, the authority for revelation (and consequently control) is strongest at the top of the corporate ladder, such as the Roman Catholic Pope or President of the Latter-Day Saints, for instance. Their scope of influence is widespread and they wield a great amount of power to control both religiously and economically and only to a somewhat smaller degree, politically. Lesser positions such as Cardinals, Archbishops, Bishops, Priests, and Deacons carry proportionately less influence depending upon the extent of their assigned charges. Each higher position provides a higher degree of economic control as well as religious control. This is a very competitive structure and requires strong capabilities and personalities, either of which may catapult one into a higher position.

An advantage of the corporate style is that it is so large a structure that it is relatively easy to "get lost" in the system and hide your incompetence for extended periods of time. Many incompetents have managed to remain in the system for their entire careers, wielding unconventional and self-destructive revelatory powers without penalty. This style also gives rise to what is known as "the good old boy" syndrome where the incompetent protects and often elevates other incompetents to protect his own incompetence from discovery and even the potential dissolution of his position within the framework of the structure.

In the congregational style of religious structure, it is generally necessary to accept some manner of commonality with other congregations as to a body of historical revelation such as the Bible in the case of Christians or Koran for Muslims. Interpretation of these traditions lies with each local leader who is assumed to be the, or at least a valid channel of revelation for the god he claims to represent.

Within this latter group fall those known as "evangelists" who generally present themselves as spokesmen for traditions rather than specific congregations. These people usually gain much power for leadership among the masses but fall short in the mechanics to exert control in specific terms, relying on individual congregational leaders to provide any necessary local controls. The popularity of the evangelist lies in direct proportion to his expertise at showmanship and often the messages he may give are often true in large part. This is possible because they maintain a distant and non-personal relationship with their control group. These people usually resort to use of radio, television, computer contacts, and mass meetings to exert their control. This is a lucrative position but requires considerable personal presence and image enhancement (focus on self during appearances). This is by nature a short-term power structure, depending almost entirely upon a single person's charisma.

It should always be remembered that people love to be entertained and made to feel righteous and important in identifiable ways and will surrender both wealth and personal freedom for opportunities to attain these ends. Often, congregational leaders and evangelists rely heavily upon the entertainment option while the corporate and historical leadership relies more heavily upon the importance of liturgical forms, historical concepts of holiness, and established rightness options.

The corporate style of religious structure is an ever-growing tradition and comes to each generation with baggage that must be either excised or enhanced for the immediate situation. In this case, position is the best base for effecting change because the higher the position, the greater the assumption that the revelation proclaimed is valid despite the historical findings. While in the Roman or Mormon tradition, the pope or president has a singular high position in declaring revelation, in some traditions such as the Anglican tradition, they are generally governed by conventions with the various bishops ruling the various dioceses with great customary independence as virtual dictators for a particular diocese. In this situation, interpretations and control can and do experience widespread abuses. Other bishops, as a defensive measure, are usually reluctant to "meddle" in another bishop's diocese and affairs lest they themselves be exposed for error.

While the congregational structure of religious commitment permits and depends upon a subjective and populist foundation and direction, the corporate structure usually has a more consistent claim for a more objective foundation based upon history rather than the whims of desire. It is true, however, that many corporate leaders foolishly believe that subjective popularity is the basis of their strength and they are inclined to permit popular whim to dictate the direction of their personal revelations which weakens their true strength that is derived from historic perception of rightness, and the importance it permits the individuals who profess it.

Many congregationally structured leaders have discovered and maintain a fidelity to the historical revelations of the general traditions they profess to their great advantage by permitting their followers to lay claim to rightness and the importance of person it permits because Man has an innate sense of belonging within history. This is a powerful abstract benefit. It also gives a sense of authenticity and power to revelations delivered by the leader in his individual congregational setting.

Liturgy Is Important

The word "liturgy" translates to "work". Most religious leaders today are working hard to simplify the liturgy they use in worship, presuming that everyone wants formal worship services to religious entities to be eased through less or simpler "work". Nothing can be further from the truth but, nonetheless, as long as people believe they are being entertained, they will continue to spend their money and be present. Entertainment is a strong motivator once a basic comfort level has been attained. What these leaders don't realize is that commitment is also lessened (having been converted to a commitment to easy entertainment), and consequently, so is their control level. This weakens them significantly should it be necessary to engage the people in some manner of direct but potentially undesirable action such as an additional act of self-denial (that is, to assume an additional burden) for a cause you may wish to support.

While it is true that Man seeks the greatest benefit for the least burden, you must also recognize that easy or simple benefits gain you small commitment and control. In a more carefree and affluent society, popular music forms and simple lyrics that are easily learned and performed with deliberately sentimental and individualaggrandizing messages attract lucrative and large followings. This orientation also has the advantage of being able to induce a mass hypnotic effect in which people are readily led to say and do things for reasons they would not necessarily consider valid in a more lucid moment. For the needs of daily problems and in times of stress and difficulties, beautiful, well ordered liturgies with glorious music and true and comforting messages filled with hope, enable the strongest and lasting attraction and control. Tragedies have a habit of occurring without notice and the economic and social well being of individuals and societies are fragile at best. Maintaining religious leadership that is both strong and lucrative requires a delicate balance, but control receives its strength from the way in which you present your personal authority as the oracle of the religious entity you profess to represent.

Beautiful and uplifting liturgies are usually difficult to perform but are worth the while to practice and present. They serve to instruct, re-enforce, and comfort the people in the practice of their religion. In the hour of need to exert control, the wise leader will have people trained by regular and judicious use of excellent liturgy to enable them to commit to and accomplish the desired end. Liberal use of classic forms of music, poetry, excellence of repeated story telling, and repetitious recitation of central themes, make them extremely effective tools to enhance liturgies and control.

Focus Is Necessary

At this point, lest you forget, it is time for a recap reminder... we have the given consideration that Man consists of creatures of limited capacity for understanding and it is the charitable and urgent duty of the gifted few of this world (of which YOU are a primary example) to organize, instruct, control, and direct the less fortunate people of the world.

Repetition is a strong reinforcement tool and should be encouraged. Muslims use the phrases "Allah is God" to which another replies, "And Mohammed is his prophet". (This offers strong potential for absolute control.)

Christians use the phrase, "He is risen!" to which another replies, "He is risen indeed!" (This is more obtuse and is subject to broader interpretations but holds a strong hope factor.) Jews repeat the Shema (Hear, O Israel...) for the same reason. (This also reinforces a strong ethnic basis.) These are primary concepts that fire loyalty and inspiration to a religious group. If you are to be an effective leader, you need to have a significant verbal summary of your chosen central teaching before your people always. Failure to do this results in a following that lacks focus and purpose. There are times when the masses become so unfocused because of the many potential leadership revelations set before them that it seems the only rallying point that can be effective is to suggest that no one revelation contains an exclusive claim to being correct. In this form, there are no absolutes and every revelation is true for the individual that holds it so. This in effect holds that the only truth is that there is no truth and that you are the person that will uphold each person's truth as valid, giving each a claim to rightness and importance and the ability to set the parameters for their individual benefits or final rewards. In recent times, this has acquired the name of "pluraform theology" and can be very effective among people uncommitted and unfocused through historical teachings and appropriate liturgies. In the 20th Century, Adolph Hitler was a master manipulator and controller. He understood that an action or lie repeated often enough evolves into a practiced truth in the minds of the people he sought to control. He attempted to create an illusion of "The Master Race". What he did not understand was that God decreed in the beginning that truth has its own inherent power for the corporate good of all creation and this led to Hitler's downfall. As noted above, if the end results of the revelations you proclaim are not truly beneficial to all people, whether adherents to your religious unit or not, the attempt at revelation will eventually fail and control will be lost as Hitler discovered when his "Third Reich" crumbled and fell physically and spiritually destroyed in defeat. His concept of a master race offended too many who did not derive benefits from the attempt to establish it.

Dealing with Truth in Revelation

One primary consideration you must take into account is that God not only exists, but also is a powerful adversary to your climb to importance and leadership if not given His due. This suggests that you must take seriously the things that are true and incorporate them into your plan for control. By this, we mean you must incorporate enough truth in your plan to accommodate the benefits the people require for retaining them under control for the period of time you intend for that control to continue in effect. Feminists and homosexuals have effectively used the idea of "Justice" and "Equality" as bywords to achieve their ends because the words carry long-standing (although often confused) powerful images associated with truth.

When deciding the length of time you are trying to retain control, there are several factors to consider. This period is usually considered in terms of a single generation unless an obligatory mentality can be established by experience and promise of inheritance of benefits such as found in monarchies and the "one-world concept" found among some wealthy and privileged families. These latter more often are established in control by economic rather than religious factors although religious factors cannot be ignored altogether. For example, philanthropies (which are perceived as a spiritual virtue in most religions) should be very public and measurably generous to retain favor of the masses in economically controllable situations.

In summary, the short-term control efforts can usually succeed for the shorter terms with less truth incorporated than the long-term efforts. This is true because people are tolerant of abuses for perceived immediate benefits until the cost of the abuse approaches or exceeds the extent of the benefits. In economic terms, benefits can be more easily measured because it primarily has to do with dollars and cents. In religiously controlled situations, spiritual terms are not as easily measured and the proverbial "straw that broke the camel's back " is an ever-present and unknown spiritual factor with which to contend.

Like it or not, God alone establishes Truth and its importance in undermining your control over people of lesser light can only be reduced temporarily and slightly by maintaining ignorance or misinformation among the people. Things which are true and of God are known among the people because their benefits are by virtue of creation experienced and recognized as good, comfortable, and of beneficial order. Control, whether economic or religious, exists in direct proportion to the benefits perceived by the people being controlled. Ignoring the reality of the benefits derived from God altogether is a fatal error in the pursuit of the charitable and urgent duty of the gifted few of this world (of which YOU may be a primary example) to organize, instruct, control, and direct the less fortunate people of the world. What you are attempting as leaders is to adjust the perception of the simpler people to accept your voice as representing the source of the benefits they enjoy and the dictator of the burdens necessary to continue the beneficent life. The more diverse the society we are dealing with, the easier it is to add individual burdens for the maintenance of the central and desirable corporate benefits perceived. These benefits, however, must have a true basis to a reasonable degree.

When assuming control of an established religious entity, introducing personal ideas is almost always possible because the people that placed you there obviously think you are more capable of control than they themselves. This substantially translates to a supposition (both to you and to them) that they are of inferior ability and understanding, and must, because they placed you in position, support you lest their own incompetence be revealed. While this is always for them a self-limiting folly indeed, you may realize you are in position to exert extensive control and derive great benefits for yourself and those whom you think will provide you the greatest support during your tenure. As an able controller, your greatest dilemma is to decide whether it is time to increase or decrease the amount of emphasis on individual or corporate benefits both for your immediate benefit and the long-range benefit of the group should you feel any obligation to do so for historical or other considerations. Here, it is necessary to have an accurate gauge of the mood of your followers and a sense of history if any long-term benefits are to be sought. Failing to discern this may lead to either a sudden, or at best, a gradual breakdown of the religious entity with the attendant loss of control and economic benefits. Consequently, a close watch on the amount of benefits and burdens being derived by the people you control on an ever-present and continuing basis is necessary to maintain optimum control over the immediate future and to insure the stability of either a short or long-term plan for control, providing adequate time to alter the benefit/burden factor required to maintain your goal.

Dangers to be Avoided

Remember, there are always other people working to usurp or change your power base by altering the follower's real or imagined perception of the benefit/burden levels and centers of your control group. These people may be either from entirely different power center groups or your own power structure. Assassination, whether actual or cultural, is effective only if the person or persons in question have not established a base perception of true benefits among a significant portion of people. Martyrs are made of this.

When your revelations become

significantly removed from that which is right, just, and true, (that widely experienced built-in of creation) your power base is weakened proportionately and your loss of power more imminent. The major error that contributes to the failure of a given leader is confusing his personal revelations and those of his supporters with truth that the people come to experience within the benefit/burden balance of their individual and corporate lives. We see the results of internal struggles historically in the waxing and waning of the traditionalist and humanist factions in the Christian churches, as well as the division between the Catholics and the Reformation Protestants, which often occurs within a single generation. Such divisions may take centuries to repair. Vigilance is always the necessary watchword in the struggle for power.

Conclusion of the Lectures

In Conclusion, Dr. Lucifer ended by thanking us for letting him give us this short overview of some of the considerations we should make when planning our careers as religious leaders at the beginning of the 21st Century. True to form, there was no test as, according to Dr. Lucifer, only the application of this information can create a worthy leader.

About the Presenter

Dr. Lucifer has been a tenured lecturer for Mankind from our earliest recorded recollections and has been a successful teacher and mentor among all races and peoples of the earth. History is full of his successes and trials as well as his failures. But in each generation, the futility of Man rises anew to rebellion against God with the desire to control himself and as many others as can be mastered. Dr. Lucifer can and does willingly accept a continuous and virtually unlimited group of new students at an unstated cost, as the essential greed that drives the desire for absolute control seems more valuable than any possible burden or cost it may demand. Truly now, will not the student believe himself more adept at the art than even his mentor? That is, after all, the nature of the beast we call sin which Dr. Lucifer himself introduced into our lives.

Author's Observation

Dr Lucifer is a very charismatic personality and his classes have been filled with many familiar persons over the years and to this present day.

It is easy to recognize his more successful students working their programs, vigorously laboring to expand their leadership and control in many fields of endeavor. The sad thing is that so many lesser lights have jumped on their band wagons hoping to gain some small benefit for their loyalty and small local influence but perhaps unaware of the price of their greed.

One of the obvious consequences of following popular opinion is readily seen in the entertainment industry. Striving to satisfy the consumer's insatiable lust for more excitement and anti-establishment material, the industry has surpassed the consumer's capacity for indecency and senselessness and is in immanent danger of collapse.

Fr. James Graner

ISBN 1-41204716-1

9 781412 047166